BADGER MATHS

PROBLEM SOLVING

FOR YEAR 3

Written and illustrated by
Andy Seed

Contents

Introduction

The aim of **Badger Maths *Problem Solving*** is to provide a valuable resource for teachers to enhance the ability of Y3 pupils in maths problem solving. The materials in the book support the National Numeracy Strategy objectives and, in particular, address the widely recognised need for a greater emphasis on using and applying mathematics.

How the book is organised

The 'Problem Solving Process' on page 4 outlines the essential broad strategies required for pupils at KS2 to solve problems in maths. It outlines a comprehensive four-step approach which includes spending time on explaining methods and reflecting.

The book is divided into six main sections, each dealing with problems which can be solved using a particular strategy. In each of these sections, there is a page of teaching notes about how the strategy works and three teaching examples which can be worked through with the whole class. These examples put into practice the four-step approach to problem solving outlined in the first chapter, and include answers and extension activities.

Each main section of the book includes five or six copiable problem solving task cards. Each of these pages consists of three illustrated problems to solve in the form of questions or activities. The problems, numbered 1 to 102, are presented at three broad levels to provide differentiation:
- Level A for pupils working below the national expectations.
- Level B for pupils working at the level of national expectations.
- Level C for pupils working above national expectations.

There is also a Copymaster for each section with prompt questions to help children work through the book's four-step approach to problem solving. This may be appropriate where children need extra help or reinforcement of the appropriate strategy.

The National Numeracy Strategy (NNS) and National Curriculum

The chart opposite gives details of where each of the book's individual numbered problems fits into the NNS framework. Most of the problems obviously come under the framework's Problem Solving strand, although some references are included twice because they also fit into other categories such as Number Sequences or Measures.

A small number of problems do not fit easily into an NNS topic and have been included under Puzzles or Real Life Problems.

There are no references to the Calculations strand of the NNS since the book is primarily concerned with using and applying maths rather than the mechanics of calculation, although it must be stressed that pupils should be encouraged to talk about the methods they use to solve problems at every opportunity.

The material in the book also addresses the Using and Applying/Problem Solving strands of each attainment target in the National Curriculum for maths at KS2.

Using this book

The book is flexibly structured and designed to be used in several different ways:
- To help teachers teach effective strategies and approaches for solving problems.
- To resource individual NNS topics, such as Length or Fractions, particularly where extra practice at using and applying maths is required.
- To provide differentiated practice at various problem solving strategies, e.g. drawing tables and using diagrams.
- For homework exercises or extra preparation for other maths assessments.

NATIONAL NUMERACY STRATEGY (NNS) LINKS

NNS Strand	Numeracy Framework topic	NNS ref	Problem number and page
Numbers and the Number System	Properties of numbers and number sequences	16-21	7 (p13), 10 (p14), 18 (p16), 19 (p26), 22 (p27), 24 (p27), 34 (p31), 37 (p41), 42 (p42), 55 (p55), 57 (p55), 58 (p56), 59 (p56), 60 (p56), 61 (p57), 62 (p57), 66 (p58), 69 (p59), 70 (p60), 74 (p69), 78 (p70), 79 (p71), 84 (p72), 89 (p82), 92 (p83), 93 (p83), 94 (p84), 97 (p85), 98 (p85), 100 (p86)
	Ratio and proportion	26-27	18 (p16), 19 (p26), 23 (p27), 27 (p28), 28 (p29), 29 (p29), 33 (p30), 35 (p31), 36 (p31), 44 (p43), 48 (p44), 56 (p55), 64 (p58), 70 (p60), 95 (p84)
Solving Problems	Making decisions	74-75	7 (p13), 14 (p15), 25 (p28), 31 (p30), 34 (p31), 37 (p41), 49 (p45), 68 (p59), 75 (p69), 76 (p70), 82 (p72), 93 (p83), 98 (p85)
	Reasoning about numbers and shapes: puzzles	78-79	1 (p11), 2 (p11), 4 (p12), 17 (p16), 22 (p27), 23 (p27), 28 (p29), 35 (p31), 39 (p41), 40 (p42), 46 (p44), 47 (p44), 50 (p45), 51 (p45), 52 (p46), 54 (p46), 55 (p55), 56 (p55), 59 (p56), 62 (p57), 63 (p57), 65 (p58), 66 (p58), 70 (p60), 72 (p60), 75 (p69), 96 (p84), 99 (p85), 100 (p86)
	Real life problems	82-83	10 (p14), 16 (p16), 19 (p26), 27 (p28), 37 (p41), 53 (p46), 67 (p59), 76 (p70), 77 (p70), 80 (p71), 81 (p71), 82 (p72), 83 (p72), 84 (p72), 85 (p73), 86 (73)
	Problems involving money	84-85	18 (p16), 26 (p28), 68 (p59), 71 (p60), 87 (p73), 102 (p86)
	Problems involving measures	86-87	8 (p13), 11 (p14), 12 (p14), 13 (p15), 16 (p16), 21 (p26), 22 (p27), 67 (p59), 101 (p86)
	Problems involving time	88-89	15 (p15), 20 (p26), 45 (p43)
Measures, Shape and Space	Length, mass and capacity	90-95	8 (p12), 11 (p14), 12 (p14), 13 (p15), 16 (p16), 21 (p26), 41 (p42)
	Properties of 3-D and 2-D shapes	102-105	4 (p12), 17 (p16), 52 (p46)
	Position and direction	108-109	3 (p11), 5 (p12), 6 (p12), 8 (p13), 9 (p13), 14 (p15), 37 (p41), 38 (p41), 43 (p43), 47 (p44), 73 (p69), 88 (p82), 90 (p82), 91 (p83)
Handling Data	Organising and interpreting data	114-117	20 (p26), 21 (p26), 22 (p27), 23 (p27), 24 (p27), 25 (p28), 26 (p28), 27 (p28), 28 (p29), 29 (p29), 30 (p29), 31 (p30), 32 (p30), 33 (p30), 34 (p51), 35 (p31), 36 (p31)

Problem Solving

THE PROBLEM SOLVING PROCESS

It is important that pupils follow a logical and systematic approach to their problem solving. Following these four steps will enable pupils to tackle problems in a structured and meaningful way.

STEP 1: UNDERSTANDING THE PROBLEM

- Encourage pupils to read the problem carefully a number of times until they fully understand what is wanted. They may need to discuss the problem with someone else or re-write it in their own words.
- Pupils should ask internal questions such as, what is the problem asking me to do, what information is relevant and necessary for solving the problem?
- They should underline any unfamiliar words and find out their meanings.
- They should select information they know and decide what is unknown or needs to be discovered. They should see if there is any unnecessary information.
- A sketch of the problem often helps their understanding.

STEP 2: PUPILS SHOULD DECIDE ON A STRATEGY OR PLAN

Pupils should decide how they will solve the problem by thinking about the different strategies that can be used. They could try to make predictions, or guesses, about the problem. Often these guesses result in generalisations which help to solve problems. Pupils should be discouraged from making wild guesses but they should be encouraged to take risks. They should always think in terms of how this problem relates to other problems that they have solved.

Some possible strategies include:
- Drawing a sketch or table.
- Acting out situations or using concrete materials.
- Organising a list.
- Identifying a pattern and extending it.
- Guessing and checking.
- Working backwards.
- Using simpler numbers to solve the problem, then applying the same methodology to the real problem.
- Writing a number sentence.
- Using logic and clues.
- Breaking the problem into smaller parts.

STEP 3: SOLVING THE PROBLEM

- Pupils should write down their ideas as they work so that they don't forget how they approached the problem.
- Their approach should be systematic as far as possible.
- If stuck, pupils should reread the problem and rethink their strategies.
- Pupils should be given the opportunity to orally demonstrate or explain how they reached an answer.

STEP 4: REFLECT

- Pupils should consider if their answer makes sense and if it has answered what was asked.
- Pupils should draw and write down their thinking processes, estimations and approach, as this gives them time to reflect on their practices. When they have an answer, they should explain the process to someone else.
- Pupils should ask themselves 'what if' to link this problem to another. This will take their exploration to a deeper level and encourage their use of logical thought processes.
- Pupils should consider if it is possible to do the problem a simpler way.

Drawing a Diagram

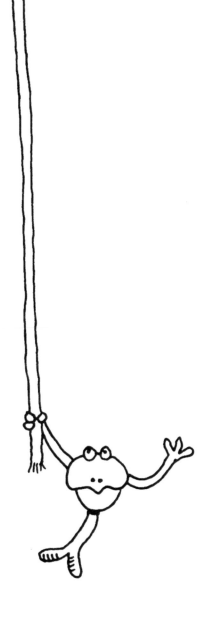

Drawing a picture of a word problem often reveals aspects of the problem that may not be apparent at first. If the situation described in the problem is difficult to visualise, a diagram, using simple symbols or pictures, may enable pupils to see the situation more easily. The diagram will also help pupils to keep track of the stages of a problem where there is more than one step.

In order to use the strategy of drawing a diagram effectively, pupils will need to develop the following skills and understanding.

Using a line to symbolise an object

Simple line drawings help pupils to visualise a situation. For example, consider the following problem: Brian drew four marks on a long stick, starting at the beginning and finishing at the end. Each mark was one metre apart. How long was the stick? In response, pupils may calculate mentally 4 x 1 = 4, but the stick is in fact three metres long. If pupils draw the stick and markers, they will be able to see this:

Using a distance line to display the information

A distance line helps to show distance or movement from one point to another. Pupils were asked to calculate how far they were from one end of a 30m path, if they were 9m from the other end. In this case, drawing the line and marking the distances on it can help them to 'see' the problem:

Mapping or showing direction

Pupils will sometimes be faced with diagrams that require them to have an understanding of direction. They will also meet problems where they are asked to plot a simple course by moving up, down, left or right on a grid. They will also need to use the compass points to direct themselves – north, south, east, west.

Pupils will also need to become familiar with measurement words which may be unfamiliar to them, such as pace. Opportunities should be given for the pupils to work out how many paces it takes to cover the length and breadth of the classroom or to pace out the playground, so they develop a means of comparison.

An ability to use a simple map is also important, as maps are sometimes used in mathematical problems such as this one:

Which is the shortest route from Bigtown to Seaby?

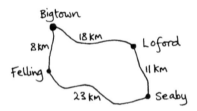

Showing the relationships between things

Pupils will find it helpful to draw diagrams and use symbols in order to visualise the relationships between things.

For example:

Joe ⟶ Brown hair
Asif ⟶ Blue eyes
Ben ⟶ Freckles

Drawing a picture

Drawing a picture can help pupils to organise their thoughts and so simplify a problem.

How many different rectangles can you make with four squares?

Drawing a Diagram

EXAMPLE 1

A baby Floop from Mars built a tower using four different Lugo bricks. The blue brick was below the green brick. The green brick was below the red brick. The yellow brick was at the bottom. Which brick was on top?

Understanding the problem

What do we know?
We know there are four bricks in the tower.
We know which brick was at the bottom.
We know that some bricks were below others.

What do we need to find out?
Questioning:
How can we find out which brick was on top?

Planning and communicating a solution

What we did
It is important that pupils develop their ability to logically explain their strategy. They should try to use mathematical language and drawings such as simple pictures, charts and diagrams in their explanation or during the problem solving process.

Some pupils will attempt to answer straight away without a diagram: some of them will be correct and some will not. Pupils should be encouraged to draw a picture so that the problem is clarified. They will then be able to see the order of the bricks.

Step-by-step explanation

First, we are told that the blue brick was below the green brick. This is straightforward to draw:

Then we are told that the green brick is below the red brick. The red brick can be added to the drawing:

Finally, we know that the yellow brick is at the bottom:

Pupils should be taught to go back to the question once the drawing is made, to check that their picture conforms to what the question says.

In this case, we can clearly see that the red brick was the one on top of the tower.

Reflecting and generalising

Once pupils have reflected on the solution, they can generalise about problems of this type and see how this solution can be applied to similar problems. Would this method work if there were five bricks or ten? Or if the bricks were in a horizontal line? They should think about how else the problem could be solved – by using Lego bricks, perhaps. Pupils should also consider if the method can be made quicker or easier.

Extension

What if five bricks were used and a white brick was above the yellow? Could we still solve the problem if one of the pieces of information was missing? Do we know which brick is at the bottom if there are four bricks and the blue is above the yellow but below the red and the red is below the green?

EXAMPLE 2

A single piece of string is cut with scissors five times. How many pieces will there be?

Understanding the problem

What do we know?
We know there is one piece of string.
We know that it is cut five times.

What do we need to find out?
Questioning:
Is the answer five? If you cut a piece of string once, how many pieces do you get? Can a diagram or picture help us to answer the question?

Planning and communicating a solution

What we did
In this case a simple diagram helps to make the answer clear. First, draw a line to represent the piece of string.

Each cut can be represented by a gap or a line across the string. These can also be numbered, to show the number of cuts.

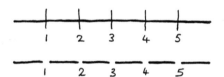

Both of these diagrams make it clear that five cuts produce six pieces.

Reflecting and generalising

Pupils who arrived at the answer five probably did not visualise the problem. This question is a good example of how a simple diagram or drawing can show a clear solution and help children to begin to see patterns. For those children who are confused by the diagram, using concrete materials may be necessary: allow them to cut a piece of string five times or use a strip of paper.

Extension

What if the string was cut six times? Nine times? 100 times? Can pupils see a pattern? It is also useful to reverse the question: how many cuts are needed to make seven pieces of string? How many cuts would give us 23 pieces? It should be emphasised throughout that the string is not doubled up at any point when it is cut. Another way to extend the question for more able pupils is to add a second factor. A piece of string is cut four times to make pieces each 6cm long. How long was the string to start with? A rope is cut into nine pieces. Each cut takes four seconds. How long will it take to cut the rope into pieces?

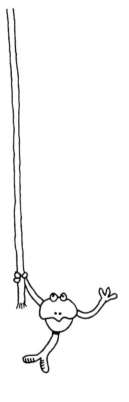

Drawing a Diagram

EXAMPLE 3

An Obble builds a robot and tells it to go to the shops which are 8km north of his house. The robot goes 2km west, then 4km north, then 2km east, then 2km north. Does it reach the shops? Draw the route on a grid to help you find the answer.

Understanding the problem

What do we know?

We know that the shops are 8km north of the house.

We know the route that the robot travels:

2km west

4km north

2km east

2km north

What do we need to find out?

Questioning:

Does the robot reach the shops 8km to the north of the house? Why will a grid help us to answer this question? Do we know what km means? How can we use the grid to help with directions?

Planning and communicating a solution

What we did

In this problem, a simple grid needs to be provided for children to draw on.

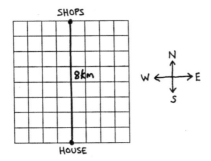

It makes sense to use each square to represent 1km. The position of the house and the shop can be marked on the grid. It's also a good idea for pupils to show the four compass directions to help them plot the course.

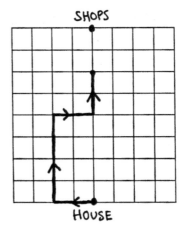

The next step is to carefully mark the robot's route on the grid. Pupils should use arrows to show direction and check their route against the question to see if it's correct. Well shown like this, it can be clearly seen that the robot does not reach the shops, having only travelled 6km north.

Reflecting and generalising

This is quite a complex problem, with a long question containing lots of information which must be understood. Pupils who do not draw an accurate route are likely to end up guessing; the problem also relies on a knowledge of compass directions. However, once children are familiar with representing routes on a simple grid, they should have no difficulty with this type of question.

Extension

What does the robot need to do to reach the shops from his final position? Apart from simply travelling 8km north, can the pupils find 3 other routes he could have taken? These should each be written as a list and each marked on a grid. Do pupils notice anything about how far east and west he must travel to reach the shops?

Drawing a Diagram

★ **Understanding the problem**
List what you know from reading the problem.

. . . .

. . . .

. . . .

★ **What do you need to find out?**
Are there any words you don't know?
Is there anything you don't understand?

. . . .

. . . .

. . . .

★ **Finding and writing the answer**
Can you draw a picture or diagram to help you find the answer?
Will a line be helpful?
Can measurements or directions be shown in your drawing?
Can you use symbols like arrows or shapes?

. . . .

. . . .

. . . .

. . . .

★ **Thinking about the problem**
What did you find?
Did you check your answer to see if it matched the question?
Was there another way you could have done it?

. . . .

. . . .

. . . .

. . . .

PROBLEM 1   Shape & Space

Level A

Pizzas on Pluto are square. If a pizza has to be cut into 6 strips, how many cuts are needed?

PROBLEM 2   Shape & Space

Level A

How many separate triangles can you make using 11 pencils?

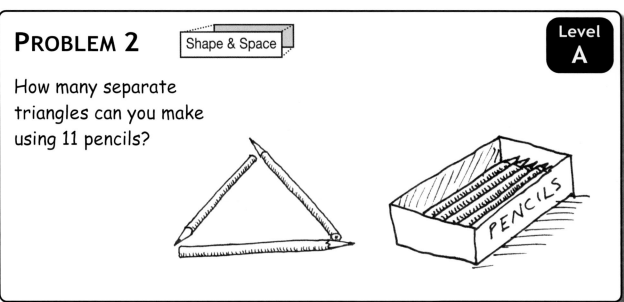

PROBLEM 3   Shape & Space

Level A

A Fimp keeps her 4 jumpers in a neat pile. The yellow one is below the blue one. The red one is above the blue one. The green one is below the yellow one. Which jumper is at the bottom of the pile?

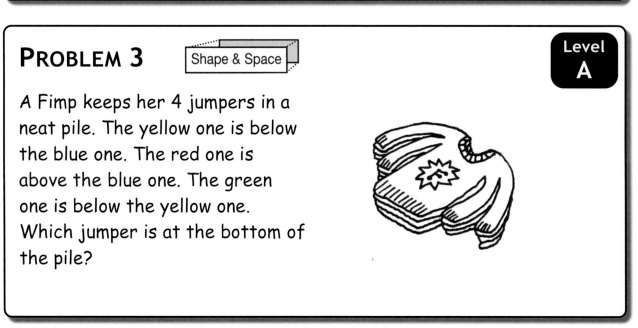

PROBLEM 4

Shape & Space

Level A

A Zozz has put 4 square tiles together to make a larger square. He then put a line of the same tiles around the outside of the square to make a bigger square. How many tiles did he use altogether?

PROBLEM 5

Shape & Space

Level A

A Little Barp spreads out 7 gold coins in a row. She then puts a silver coin between each gold coin. How many coins are in the row altogether?

PROBLEM 6

Shape & Space

Level A

A Grunf sandwich is made of 4 slices of bread. There are 3 pieces of cheese between each slice of bread. How many pieces of cheese are needed to make a Grunf sandwich?

PROBLEM 7 Numbers 1 2 3

Level B

Phop planted 3 rows of onions, with 6 in each row. Birds ate half of the first row. How many onions were left altogether?

PROBLEM 8 Shape & Space

Level B

A Jiva-Jiva went for a walk from her house. She walked north for 2 kilometres, then west for 1 kilometre, then south for 1 kilometre, then east for 2 kilometres.

Did she finish at home?

PROBLEM 9 Numbers 1 2 3

Level B

A Brip walks up 9 steps of a staircase then goes back 4 steps to pick up something she has dropped. She then walks 8 steps to the top. How many steps does the staircase have?

PROBLEM 10 — Shape & Space — Level B

Ziggos make cans of rock juice to sell to other planets. They pack the cans in square boxes, 4 cans wide. How many cans does each box hold?

PROBLEM 11 — Measures — Level B

A swimming pool is 10 metres long and 6 metres wide. Each day a Yox walks around it to check for beetles. How far does he walk each day?

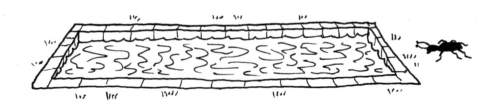

PROBLEM 12 — Measures — Level B

A Gupp is making a new garden fence. It will be made up of 12 vertical posts, each 2 metres apart. The posts will be joined by wires. How long will the fence be?

PROBLEM 13 | Measures |

Level
C

The houses on planet Moobu are 3 metres apart. Each house is 10 metres wide. How long is a row of 5 houses on Moobu?

PROBLEM 14 | Shape & Space |

Level
C

A Quock chess board is a rectangle covered in squares. It has a centre square with 2 squares either side of it in one direction and 3 squares either side of it in the other direction. How many squares cover the board?

PROBLEM 15 | Measures |

Level
C

On a small planet, a group of Buvvers are making fishing rods by tying sticks together. It takes 3 minutes to tie 2 sticks together. How long will it take to join 6 sticks to make a long fishing rod?

PROBLEM 16 | Measures

Level C

Glob, Glab, Glub and Gleb are four aliens waiting in a long queue. Glob is at the front. Glab is 6m behind him. Glub is 18m behind Glob. Gleb is 20m behind Glub. How far apart are Glab and Gleb?

PROBLEM 17 | Shape & Space

Level C

A Slimp arranged 15 matchsticks to make 5 squares like this one. How did he do it?

 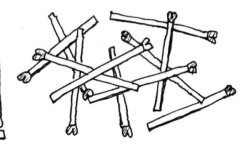

PROBLEM 18 | Numbers 1 2 3

Level C

On the planet Mymm, the unit of money is called the fip. It is planned to plant a line of 14 trees on Mymm, costing 52 fips in total. The line starts with a noggo tree and every third tree is also a noggo tree, costing 5 fips. How much does each of the other trees cost?

Answers to Task Cards
Drawing a Diagram

PROBLEM 1

5 cuts are needed to cut the pizza into six strips.

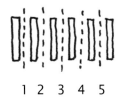

1 2 3 4 5

PROBLEM 2

It is possible to make 3 triangles with 11 pencils.

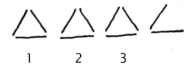

1   2   3

PROBLEM 3

The green jumper is at the bottom of the pile.

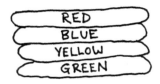

PROBLEM 4

The Zozz used 16 tiles in total.

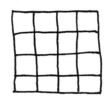

4 x 4 = 16

PROBLEM 5

There are 13 coins in the row.

7 + 6 = 13

PROBLEM 6

9 pieces of cheese are needed for a Grunf sandwich.

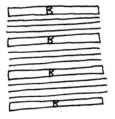

3 x 3 = 9

PROBLEM 7

15 onions were left.

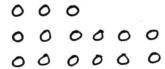

6 + 6 + 3 = 15

PROBLEM 8

No, the Jiva-Jiva did not finish at home.

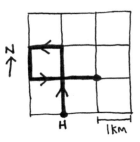

PROBLEM 9

The staircase has 13 steps.

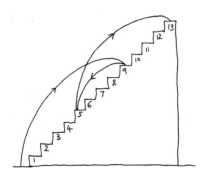

PROBLEM 10

Each box holds 16 cans.

$4 \times 4 = 16$

PROBLEM 11

The Yox walks 32m.

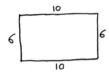

$10 + 10 + 6 + 6 = 32$

PROBLEM 12

The fence will be 22m long.

$11 \times 2 = 22$

PROBLEM 13

A row of five houses is 62m long.

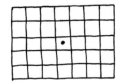

$5 \times 10 = 50$
$4 \times 3 = 12$
$50 + 12 = 62$

PROBLEM 14

A Quock chessboard has 35 squares.

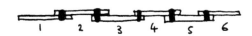

$7 \times 5 = 35$

PROBLEM 15

It will take 15 minutes to make a fishing rod with six sticks.

5 joins are needed: $5 \times 3 = 15$

PROBLEM 16

Glab and Gleb are 32m apart.

$20 + 12 = 32$

PROBLEM 17

(or an equivalent arrangement)

PROBLEM 18

The other trees cost 3 fips each.

The noggos cost $5 \times 5 = 25$ fips
$52 - 25 = 27$ so the other trees cost 27 fips in total.
There are 9 other trees: $27 \div 9 = 3$

Drawing a Table

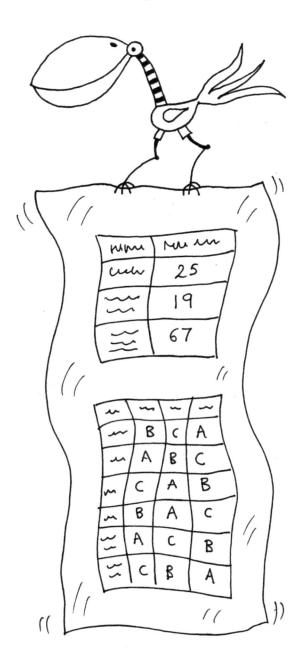

Drawing a Table

When a problem contains information that has more than one characteristic, an effective strategy is to set out that information so that it can be easily understood and so that the relationships between one variable and another become clear. A table makes it easy to see what information is there, and what information is missing. When a table is drawn up, the information often shows a pattern, or part of a solution, which can then be completed. Pupils will usually have to create some of the information in order to complete the table and so solve the problem.

Using a table can help reduce the possibility of mistakes or repetitions.

Teachers will frequently need to assist pupils to decide how to classify and divide up the information in the problem and then how to construct an appropriate table. Teachers should give advice on how many rows and columns are needed and what headings to use in the table.

Certain skills and understandings should be reinforced before pupils begin to work with this strategy.

Deciding on the number of columns

When drawing up a table, the very first important step is for pupils to read the problem carefully and establish how many columns are required. This depends on the number of variables in the question. Although, at Y3, tables are likely to be relatively simple, with just two or three columns, identifying the variables is not an easy skill to develop and some pupils will need plenty of help to develop it. First they should decide how many factors are involved in each problem, then discuss whether the factor needs a column or row. Pupils also need to learn the importance of clear headings for columns and rows, so that the exact contents of the table are clear.

For example: A box has five plastic shapes in it. Some are triangles and some are squares. There are 17 corners in the box altogether. How many triangles and how many squares are in the box?

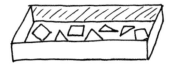

Pupils will need to draw up a table that has three columns.

Number of triangles	Number of squares	Number of corners
5	0	15
4	1	16
3	2	17
2	3	18
1	4	19
0	5	20

Setting out tables

Sometimes it may be easier for pupils to set out information horizontally rather than vertically. Show pupils how some sets of information can be arranged either way, as long as the headings are clear.

For example: A Powi eats three eggs a day for a week, starting on Monday. How many eggs has it eaten in total by the end of Saturday?

A two column (or two row) table is required and this can be arranged vertically or horizontally.

Day	Mon	Tue	Wed	Thur	Fri	Sat
Total eggs eaten	3	6	9	12	15	18

The key word here is total, as the Powi actually eats three eggs each day.

Teaching Examples
Drawing a Table

Seeing patterns

Once pupils understand how to set out tables, they should be able to see patterns emerge in the numbers quite quickly. Tables provide a framework which pupils can use to develop understanding of concepts such as multiples. They can also help to remove confusion when a problem requires counting or calculation which may be difficult to carry out mentally.

For example: A Montu has ten bars of toffee. Starting in March, she eats one each month. What month will she run out?

Month	Number of bars left
March	9
April	8
May	7
June	6
July	5
August	4
September	3
October	2
November	1
December	0

A table like this enables pupils to see patterns and understand how to find the answer to the problem quickly.

Using patterns

Tables can be used to establish many different kinds of patterns. The information presented in the problem can be listed in the table and then examined to see if there is a pattern.

For example: A Yoggle picks plums with his friend, the Demp. For every plum the Yoggle picks, the Demp picks five. How many plums will the Yoggle have when the Demp has 30?

Two columns are needed in this case, as there are two variables. Once the number patterns are established, the answer can be extracted quite simply.

Plums picked by the Yoggle	Plums picked by the Demp
1	5
2	10
3	15
4	20
5	25
6	30

The Yoggle will have six plums when the Demp has 30.

Drawing a Table

EXAMPLE 1

On the planet Yump, they use the same coins as we do. How many ways can a 10p coin be changed into 2p and 1p coins?

Understanding the problem

What do we know?

That the coins are the same as we use.
That we can only change the 10p for 2ps and 1ps.

What do we need to find out?

Questioning:
How can we write down all of the different combinations of 2p coins and 1p coins so that we don't miss any? Can we follow a pattern?

Planning and communicating a solution

What we did

It is possible to write a list of each combination in the following form:

2p + 2p + 2p + 2p + 1p + 1p = 10p
1p + 1p + 1p + 1p + 2p + 2p + 2p = 10p

However, this is a long-winded method and it is also not systematic. If we use a table, we can record all of the different coin combinations much more simply. We need two columns, one for the number of 2p coins and one for the number of 1p coins. Then it is just a matter of recording totals which equal 10p (each row should add up to 10p).

Number of 2p coins	Number of 1p coins
5	0
4	2
3	4
2	6
1	8
0	10

There are six different ways that a 10p coin can be changed for 2p and 1p coins.

Reflecting and generalising

Notice how a system has been used here: the first row records the maximum number of 2p coins and then the next row records the next highest number of 2p coins. Likewise, the table would work just as well to start with zero 2p coins and work up, or think about the 1p coins first and arrange those in ascending or descending order. It is important to encourage pupils to be systematic like this or mistakes can occur. The table above also reveals some interesting number patterns which can lead to discussion and bolster understanding of concepts such as even numbers.

Extension

The problem can be extended by including 5p coins as well, or by finding out how many ways a 20p coin can be changed for 2ps and 1ps. For larger numbers, use a £1 or £2 coin in place of the 10p.

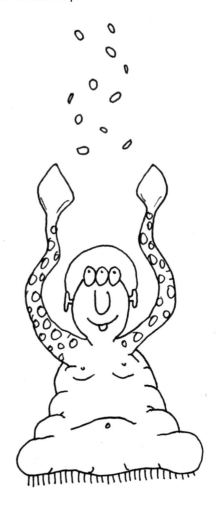

Drawing a Table

EXAMPLE 2

Lots of Plooks went on a picnic. Each Plook brought three pies and four cakes to eat. How many cakes were there when there were 15 pies?

Understanding the problem

What do we know?

Each Plook brought three pies and four cakes. Several Plooks went on the picnic.

What do we need to find out?

Questioning:

Do we know how many Plooks were there? Each time a Plook arrives, how many more pies are there? How many more cakes? How many pies are there when there are two Plooks at the picnic? How many cakes? What about when three arrive? How can we put this information into a table?

Planning and communicating a solution

What we did

The simplest thing to do is to record how many pies and cakes there are for one Plook, then two, then three and so on. We can then look at the numbers and work out the patterns. A good way to approach the problem is to make a table with three columns: one for the number of Plooks, one for pies and one for puddings, each showing the totals.

Number of Plooks	Total number of pies	Total number of cakes
1	3	4
2	6	8
3	9	12
4	12	16
5	15	20

The table clearly shows that there will be 20 cakes when there are 15 pies.

Reflecting and generalising

What initially might seem quite a difficult and confusing problem can be made clear and straightforward by creating the right table. Pupils will be able to extend the patterns and extract other information from it. Once more, it is essential to stress the importance of the column headings: the word total is significant, as in previous examples.

Extension

How many pies would there be if there were 28 cakes at the party? How many cakes would there be if there were 30 pies? What about 300 pies? Can there be 23 pies at the picnic (assuming none are eaten!)? Why? How many Plooks are at the picnic if there are 56 items of food altogether? (This last question may require a fourth column in the table.) The problem can also be extended by varying the number of items brought by each Plook.

Drawing a Table

EXAMPLE 3

A Trawk cuts up a tree trunk to make some logs. On the first day, he cuts the tree trunk in half. On the second day, he cuts each piece into two. He carries on each day, cutting all the pieces of the tree trunk into two. How many pieces will he have after a week?

Understanding the problem

What do we know?
A tree trunk is being cut up for logs.
On the first day, the tree trunk is cut in half.
Each day, all of the pieces are cut in half.

What do we need to find out?
Questioning:
How many pieces will there be on the first day? How many will there be on the second day? How can we record the number of logs each day?

Planning and communicating a solution

What we did
Create a simple two-column table. The first column records the number of days that are passing; the second column records the number of logs. With this type of question, it can help to also use concrete materials to ensure that the pattern is correct: a paper 'tree trunk' can be cut up with scissors or plasticine can be used. Pupils should soon discover the doubling pattern and be able to extend it mentally until the numbers become too large.

Day	Total number of logs
1	2
2	4
3	8
4	16
5	32
6	64
7	128

The Trawk had 128 logs at the end of the week.

Reflecting and generalising

The solution here, using a simple table, produces a clear pattern which can quickly be extended. It ensures that numbers are recorded logically and systematically.

Extension

Use a calculator to discover how many logs the Trawk would have at the end of two weeks. On what day will he have 1000 logs? What if he cuts each piece into three instead of two?

Drawing a Table

★ **Understanding the problem**
List what you know from reading the problem.

. . . .

. . . .

. . . .

★ **What do you need to find out?**
Are there any words you don't know?
Is there anything you don't understand?

. . . .

. . . .

. . . .

★ **Finding and writing the answer**
How many sets of numbers are there?
How many columns will the table need to have?
What heading will each column need?

★ **Thinking about the problem**
What did you find?
Did you check your answer to see if it matched the question?
Was there another way you could have done it?

. . . .

. . . .

. . . .

. . . .

PROBLEM 19 Numbers 1 2 3

Level
A

Some Kriks are invited to a party. Each Krik brings three presents. How many Kriks will need to go to the party so that there are at least 20 presents?

PROBLEM 20 Shape & Space

Level
A

A Binx has 11 carrots. Starting on a Friday, she eats 1 carrot a day.

Which day of the week will she run out on?

PROBLEM 21 Shape & Space

Level
A

A Yaj grows half a metre each day. How much will it grow in 5 days?

PROBLEM 22 — Measures

Level A

A meteor flying through space is 50cm long. Each week it loses 3cm. How long will it be after 4 weeks?

PROBLEM 23 — Numbers 1 2 3

Level A

Hupp ate 8 rolls on Monday then half as many on Tuesday. He ate half as many as that on Wednesday. How many did he eat on Thursday if he ate half as many as on Wednesday?

PROBLEM 24 — Numbers 1 2 3

Level A

A Nerp has 1 eye and 4 ears. How many eyes and ears will 8 Nerps have altogether?

PROBLEM 25 Numbers 1 2 3

Level B

2 types of creature live on the planet Nez. Wompos have 2 legs and Jums have 5 legs. If there are 17 legs in a house, how many Wompos and Jums are there in the house?

PROBLEM 26 Measures

Level B

Wiffas have the same money as us. How many ways can a Wiffa change a 50p coin into 10p and 5p coins?

PROBLEM 27 Numbers 1 2 3

Level B

A Querp has 24 bags of moon rock. The next day he gives away half of them. Each day he gives away half of all the bags he has. How long before he has only 3 bags left?

PROBLEM 28 Numbers 1 2 3

A Zeg notices that 1 spaceship has 3 round windows and 2 square ones. If the Zeg can see 30 windows altogether, how many spaceships are there?

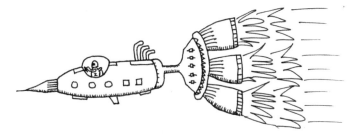

PROBLEM 29 Numbers 1 2 3

Oom plants have 2 black flowers and 1 white one. If there are 12 Oom flowers altogether in a field, how many will be white?

PROBLEM 30 Numbers 1 2 3

On the first day of the holidays, 10 aliens visited the planet Ticatic. The next day, 12 aliens visited and, the day after that, 14 aliens visited. If this pattern continued, how many aliens visited on the eighth day of the holidays?

PROBLEM 31 — Numbers 1 2 3

Level C

A Rillet collects rocks. He starts with 5 rocks and each day he collects 1 more than he did the day before. How many rocks will he have after a week?

PROBLEM 32 — Measures

Level C

Each day, a Loofy spends 6 minutes jogging, 2 minutes stretching and 4 minutes skipping. How many days will it take for her to do an hour's exercise?

PROBLEM 33 — Numbers 1 2 3

Level C

Gribbies and Ferts love eating worms. Each time the Gribbie eats 3 worms, the Fert eats 7 worms. By the time the Fert has eaten 42 worms, how many will the Gribbie have eaten?

PROBLEM 34 | Numbers 1 2 3

Level C

A giant Fopso ate some icebergs over 4 days, starting Monday. Each day he ate 6 more than he had the day before. If he ate 24 on Thursday, how many did he eat altogether?

PROBLEM 35 | Numbers 1 2 3

Level C

Starting Monday, Skagg and Fragg gather mushrooms. Skagg picks 3 each day and Fragg picks 5 every other day. How many will they have by the end of Saturday?

PROBLEM 36 | Numbers 1 2 3

Level C

The flying saucer factory on Rymbu makes 7 flying saucers a day. 3 of these have a sunroof. If 49 flying saucers are made, how many will have sunroofs?

Drawing a Table

PROBLEM 19

7 Kriks will need to go to the party.

Number of Kriks	Number of presents
1	3
2	6
3	9
4	12
5	15
6	18
7	21

PROBLEM 20

She will run out of carrots on Tuesday.

Day	F	Sa	Su	M	Tu	W
No.	11	10	9	8	7	6
Day	Th	F	Sa	Su	M	Tu
No.	5	4	3	2	1	0

PROBLEM 21

The Yaj will grow 2½ metres.

Day	Total amount grown (metres)
1	½
2	1
3	1½
4	2
5	2½

PROBLEM 22

The meteor will be 38cm long.

Week	Length of meteor at end of week (cm)
1	47
2	44
3	41
4	38

PROBLEM 23

Hupp ate 1 roll on Thursday.

Day	No. rolls
Mon	8
Tues	4
Wed	2
Thurs	1

PROBLEM 24

8 Nerps will have 40 eyes and ears in total.

Number of Nerps	Number of eyes	Number of ears	Total eyes and ears
1	1	4	5
2	2	8	10
3	3	12	15
4	4	16	20
5	5	20	25
6	6	24	30
7	7	28	35
8	8	32	40

PROBLEM 25

There are either 3 Jums and 1 Wompo in the house, or 1 Jum and 6 Wompos.

Number of Wompos	Number of Jums	Total Legs

The answers can be revealed through trial and error using the table above.

PROBLEM 26

There are 6 ways to change a 50p coin for 10p and 5p coins.

Number of 10p coins	Number of 5p coins
0	10
1	8
2	6
3	4
4	2
5	0

PROBLEM 27

After 4 days he will have only 3 bags left.

Day	Number of bags
1	24
2	12
3	6
4	3

Answers to Task Cards
Drawing a Table

PROBLEM 28
6 spaceships will have a total of 30 windows.

Ships	No. round windows	No. square windows	Total windows
1	3	2	5
2	6	4	10
3	9	6	15
4	12	8	20
5	15	10	25
6	18	12	30

PROBLEM 29
4 of the flowers will be white.

Plants	No. black flowers	No. white flowers	Total flowers
1	2	1	3
2	4	2	6
3	6	3	9
4	8	4	12

PROBLEM 30
24 aliens visited on the eighth day.

Day	Number of visitors
1	10
2	12
3	14
4	16
5	18
6	20
7	22
8	24

PROBLEM 31
The Rillet will have collected 56 rocks after a week.

Day	No. rocks collected	Total no. of rocks
1	5	5
2	6	11
3	7	18
4	8	26
5	9	35
6	10	45
7	11	56

PROBLEM 32
It will take 5 days for the Loofy to do an hour's exercise.

Day	Mins jog	Mins stretch	Mins skip	Total time
1	6	2	4	12
2	12	4	8	24
3	18	6	12	36
4	24	8	16	48
5	30	10	20	60

PROBLEM 33
The Gribbie will have eaten 18 worms.

Worms eaten by Gribbie	Worms eaten by Fert
3	7
6	14
9	21
12	28
15	35
18	42

PROBLEM 34
The giant Fopso ate 60 icebergs.

Day	Icebergs eaten	Total eaten
Mon	6	6
Tues	12	18
Wed	18	36
Thurs	24	60

PROBLEM 35
They will have 33 mushrooms by Saturday's end.

Day	Total by Skagg	Total by Fragg	Total by both
M	3	5	8
Tu	6	5	11
W	9	10	19
Th	12	10	22
F	15	15	30
Sa	18	15	33

PROBLEM 36
21 flying saucers will have a sunroof.

No. of flying saucers	No. with a sunroof
7	3
14	6
21	9
28	12
35	15
42	18
49	21

Acting it Out
or
Using Concrete Material

Acting it Out or Using Concrete Material

Sometimes it can be hard for pupils to gain a concrete understanding of an abstract problem. To assist pupils who are finding it difficult to visualise a problem, or the procedure necessary for its solution, it is often helpful to use objects (concrete material) to represent the people or things in the problem. A variety of objects such as counters, blocks, pencils or rubbers can be used to symbolise people or places. These objects can be moved through the steps of the problem. It is important to chart this movement to keep track of the process.

It can also be very helpful for pupils to act out the roles of the different participants in the problem.

Certain skills and understandings should be reinforced before pupils begin to work with this strategy.

MOVING FROM ONE POSITION TO ANOTHER

If the characters, or objects, featured in a problem move around a lot, it can be confusing and difficult to solve. By getting pupils to act it out, the movements in the problem can be plotted.

For example: a Lomp was checking a row of cabbages in her garden. Starting at one end, she checked six cabbages, then noticed a bug land on one she had passed. She went back four cabbages to shoo the bug, then she walked past nine cabbages to the end of the row. How many cabbages were there in the row?

Now ask the pupils to act out the problem. Put a row of objects (say 14 or so) on the floor to represent the cabbages. Indicate which is the end from which the Lomp started her inspection. Nominate a child to be the Lomp. He or she should start at one end of the row and walk past six 'cabbages', then walk back past four of them. Finally, ask the pupil to walk past nine 'cabbages' and the class can see clearly that the pupil walked past 11 cabbages in total.

A similar approach can be taken with the following problem: A Gruckle is climbing up a five metre wall. Each hour it climbs two metres and then rests for one hour. During its rest, the Gruckle slips back one metre. How long till it reaches the top of the wall?

Draw a five metre line on the ground and use pupils or an object to show the movements of the Gruckle. Ask other pupils to count one hour for every two metres the Gruckle moves forward and one hour for each metre it slips back while resting.

Teaching Examples
Acting it Out or Using Concrete Material

Working with amounts

Often amounts of money or quantities of substances are exchanged between the characters in a problem. Unless a means of visualising or acting out the problem is used, the results can be very confusing. This method is particularly helpful with more complex exchanges, where pupils may not be able to write or explain the operations accurately.

For example: For a visit to Earth, Rho, Bho and Dho have been given £70 to spend between them. Rho was allowed twice as much as Bho, and Bho was allowed twice as much as Dho. How much money did each one have?

Ask three pupils to act out the parts of the aliens and use £70 play money.

Start by giving Dho an estimated amount:
- ☐Give Dho £20.
- ☐Bho should be given twice as much:
- ☐   2 x £20 = £40
- ☐Rho should be given twice as much as Bho:
- ☐   2 x £40 = £80
- ☐Total: £20 + £40 + £80 = £140.
- ☐This total is too high.

Next try a lower amount.
- ☐Give Dho £10.
- ☐Bho should be given twice as much:
- ☐2 x £10 = £20
- ☐Rho should be given twice as much as Bho:
- ☐2 x £20 = £40
- ☐Total: £10 + £20 + £40 = £70.
- ☐This is correct.

Specific quantities

Sometimes a problem requires pupils to measure out an exact quantity, but they do not have access to containers which can hold the correct amount. The pupils must come up with a way to accurately measure the required quantity using the containers they have. Acting out the process makes it easier to work out a solution.

For example: If exactly one litre of water has to be measured out but I only have a two litre and a three litre container, what can I do?

Pupils will see the solution if they can act out the process of filling the three litre container then using it to fill the two litre container so that one litre remains.

Using concrete materials

When a problem contains large numbers (of objects or people), it may not be practical to use pupils to act it out. Using concrete materials, such as counters or blocks, will assist pupils to work through the process.

For example: In a queue of 38 Thabs visiting the cinema, every fourth Thab is given a leaflet. How many leaflets were handed out?

This problem is straightforward to solve with counters or blocks and the process will enable pupils to see patterns that will help them in learning to find alternative solutions.

Acting it Out or Using Concrete Material

EXAMPLE 1

Slup lives on the middle floor of a block of flats. Marf lives two floors below her. There are three floors beneath Marf, including the ground floor. How many floors does the block of flats have?

Understanding the problem

What do we know?
Slup lives on the middle floor.
Marf is two floors below Slup.
There are three floors below Marf.

What do we need to find out?
Questioning:
How many floors are there below Slup?
How many above Slup?
How many floors altogether?

Planning and communicating a solution

What we did
Use two different types or colours of counters/blocks. Use one colour to show Slup's position on the middle floor.

Marf is two floors below Slup so mark these two floors with two counters placed in a vertical line below the Slup counter, with Marf's counter the same colour as Slup's one.

Next add three more counters to show the three floors below Marf. It is now possible to count how many floors there are below Slup in total (five) and to add counters for this many above her.

There are now five counters above Slup and five below her, giving 11 floors altogether.

Reflecting and generalising

It is surprisingly easy for pupils to make errors with problems like this, even though they seem quite straightforward. Using concrete materials – in this case counters – shows clearly what the answer is. The problem can also be solved by drawing a diagram or picture but, for many pupils, using concrete materials is reassuring and they are easy to move around.

Extension

The problem can be extended by introducing other characters or increasing the number of floors. Questions can also be asked about the relative positions of characters: if Slup's sister Jip moves onto the floor four above Slup, how many floors are there between Jip and Marf? If six more floors were added, how many floors would Slup have to move to still be on the middle floor?

Acting it Out or Using Concrete Material

EXAMPLE 2

An Uvu has three jars marked A, B and C, each containing cookies. He takes two cookies from jar C and puts them in jar B. Jar A now has twice as many cookies as jar B. If there are 11 cookies altogether, how many were in each of the three jars to begin with?

Understanding the problem

What do we know?
There are three jars with cookies in, marked A, B and C.
There are 11 cookies altogether.
When two cookies are moved from C to B, jar A has twice as many as B.

What do we need to find out?
Questioning:
How many cookies might be in each jar? Can we say what the minimum number of cookies in each jar must be at the start?

Planning and communicating a solution

What we did
Use three pieces of paper to represent the three jars. Mark these A, B and C respectively. Then 11 counters can be used to represent the 11 cookies.

We do not know how many cookies are in each jar to begin with but we do know that there must be at least two in jar C and some in Jar A also. There may or may not be some in jar B.

The best way to begin is to estimate the starting numbers, then to carry out the movement of cookies in the problem and to see what we get as a result.

Put 8 in jar A, 1 in jar B and 2 in jar C. If we move 2 cookies from C to B, we have A 8, B 3, C 0: there are more than twice as many cookies in A as in B now.

Try A 6, B 2, C 3. If we move two from C to B this time, we get A 6, B 4, C 1: it is still not correct because we need to have three cookies in B.

Try A 6, B 1, C 4. After moving two cookies from C to B, we have A 6, B 3, C2: A is now twice B, so the above starting numbers are correct.

Reflecting and generalising

This problem is particularly difficult to solve mentally but using concrete materials allows us to use an effective trial and error system to arrive at the right solution. As with the other examples, pupils will begin to spot patterns and see relationships. Some will notice that there cannot be eight cookies in A at the end because there would need to be four in B and 8 + 4 = 12, which is not possible if we only have 11 to start with.

Extension

There are numerous possible permutations involving this scenario. If there is one more cookie in jars A and B together than in jar C, how many are in each? If there are three more in B than A and two more in C than B, how many in each? The numbers of cookies can also be increased and further jars added.

Acting it Out or Using Concrete Material

EXAMPLE 3

There are five shapes in a line. The square is immediately to the left of the circle. The triangle is between the circle and the rectangle. The star is immediately to the right of the rectangle. Which shape is in the middle?

Understanding the problem

What do we know?
There are five shapes in a line.
The square is to the left of the circle.
The triangle is between the circle and the rectangle.
The star is to the right of the rectangle.

What do we need to find out?
Questioning:
Which shape is in the middle? How can we be sure? How can we represent the shapes?

Planning and communicating a solution

What we did
Five children each took the place of a shape. They each held a card with their shape drawn on it.

The child with the square stands to the left of the child with the circle (that is, the left of the audience facing them).

The triangle must be the other side of the circle and the rectangle must be right of the triangle, so those two children can take their places in the line.

The star then stands to the right of the rectangle, revealing that the triangle is the shape in the middle of the five.

Reflecting and generalising

What seems to be a difficult problem to envisage can be quickly solved by acting out. Plastic shapes or shapes drawn on paper can also be used to represent the shapes, of course.

Extension

Further shapes can be added or the relationship between them can be described in different ways. What if the rectangle is three places to the right of the circle and the shape furthest to the left is the triangle; if the square is next to the circle, where is the star?

Acting it Out or Using Concrete Material

★ **Understanding the problem**
List what you know.

. . . .

. . . .

. . . .

★ **What do you need to find out?**
Is there anything you don't understand?
What are you being asked to find out?

. . . .

. . . .

. . . .

★ **Finding and writing the answer**
Are you moving the position of something?
Are you using money or amounts of something?
Can you use objects or counters to represent things?
Can you act out the problem in any way?

. . . .

. . . .

. . . .

. . . .

★ **Thinking about the problem**
What did you find?
Did you check your answer to see if it matched the question?
Was there another way you could have done it?

. . . .

. . . .

. . . .

. . . .

PROBLEM 37 Shape & Space

Level A

Some aliens are lining up for a photo. Kawb is in the middle of the line. She has 3 aliens to her left. How many aliens are in the line?

PROBLEM 38 Shape & Space

Level A

In a pile of 4 different coins, the 10p is on top of the 2p. The 2p coin is between the £1 coin and the 10p. The 50p is above the 10p. Which coin is at the bottom of the pile?

PROBLEM 39 Numbers 123

Level A

A Martian found 11 bones and put them into 3 piles. The first pile had 1 more bone than the second pile. The third pile had twice as many bones as the first pile. How many bones were in each pile?

PROBLEM 40 Measures

Level A

4 aliens weighed themselves. Yav was heavier than Gronc, but not as heavy as Blizz. Shup was heavier than Blizz. Who was the second heaviest?

PROBLEM 41 Measures

Level A

Goxx has a thirsty plant which needs 2 litres of water each day. She only has a 3 litre jug and a 5 litre bottle. How can she measure out 2 litres?

PROBLEM 42 Numbers 123

Level A

Ommu has 12 pears. She keeps half of them and shares the rest between 3 friends. How many pears does each friend get?

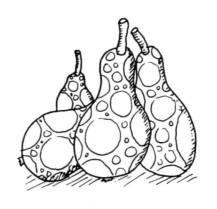

PROBLEM 43   Numbers 123

Level B

Glort's diary was in the middle of a pile of other books. There was an atlas 2 books above the diary and there were 4 books on top of the atlas. How many books were in the pile altogether?

PROBLEM 44   Numbers 123

Level B

10 Hinks are sitting in a circle for a game. Starting with the oldest Hink, every second one gets a bat and every third one gets a ball. How many Hinks don't get anything?

PROBLEM 45   Measures

Level B

A Flobble lizard was climbing up a slippery river bank 6 metres high. Each minute it climbed 2 metres, then rested for a minute. During its rest, the lizard slipped back 1 metre. How long did it take the Flobble lizard to climb the river bank?

PROBLEM 46 — Measures

Level
B

Quig has a 2 litre jug of toad soup. He pours half of the soup into a bowl. He eats half of what is in the bowl then pours what is left back into the jug. How much soup is in the jug?

PROBLEM 47 — Numbers 1 2 3

Level
B

A Smonk was standing on the bottom rung of a ladder. He climbed up 8 rungs, then went back down 5 rungs to pick up a tissue he had dropped. He then climbed up 3 more rungs, so that he was on the middle rung of the ladder. How many rungs did the ladder have in total?

PROBLEM 48 — Numbers 1 2 3

Level
B

A Drittle sees a line of 33 trees. It eats the first tree then eats every fifth tree. How many trees are left?

Acting it Out or Using Concrete Material

PROBLEM 49 | Measures | Level C

A Wurf has a 2 litre and a 3 litre container. She claims that she can measure out 1 litre, 2 litres, 3 litres, 4 litres and 5 litres using them. Is this possible?

PROBLEM 50 | Numbers 12₃ | Level C

Three Vumps collected 19 nuts to eat. The big Vump ate 2 more than the medium Vump and 3 more than the little Vump. How many nuts did each Vump eat?

PROBLEM 51 | Shape & Space | Level C

Some aliens have unwisely built a house on a volcano which is about to blow. There are 2 Narfs and 2 Spliggs in the house. They have a jetcopter to fly to a safe mountain nearby but it can only carry 1 Narf or 2 Spliggs at a time. They can all fly the jetcopter but how can they all escape their doom?

Acting it Out or Using Concrete Material

PROBLEM 52 | Shape & Space

Level C

A Wexi is making patterns with rectangular tiles. Each tile is 3 times longer than it is wide. How many different rectangles can the Wexi make using 3 rectangular tiles? (Clue: he doesn't have to use all of the tiles each time).

PROBLEM 53 | Measures

Level C

On the planet Veen, the unit of money is the yit. A Tazzle bought 2 hats for 12 yits each. He then sold 1 of them for 18 yits and the other for 10 yits. The following week, he bought 1 hat back for 11 yits, then sold it again for 6 yits. Overall, how much money did he make or lose on the hats?

PROBLEM 54 | Numbers 123

Level C

Chau puts 40 bricks into 3 bags. The second bag has 8 times more bricks than the first bag. The first bag has 10 fewer bricks than the third bag. How many bricks in each bag?

Acting it Out or Using Concrete Material

PROBLEM 37

There are 7 aliens in the line.

A A A K A A A

PROBLEM 38

The £1 coin is bottom of the pile.

50p
10p
2p
£1

PROBLEM 39

There were 3 bones in the first pile, 2 in the second pile and 6 in the third pile.

PROBLEM 40

Blizz was the second heaviest alien. Order (heaviest first): Shup, Blizz, Yav, Gronc.

PROBLEM 41

She can fill the 5 litre bottle then pour 3 litres from it into the jug, leaving 2 litres.

PROBLEM 42

Each friend receives two pears.

PROBLEM 43

There were 13 books in the pile.

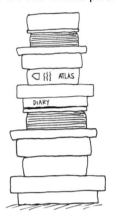

PROBLEM 44

3 Hinks do not get anything.

Hink number	Object given
1 (oldest)	
2	bat
3	ball
4	bat
5	
6	bat, ball
7	
8	bat
9	ball
10	bat

PROBLEM 45

The lizard took 9 minutes to climb the river bank: 5 minutes climbing, 4 resting.

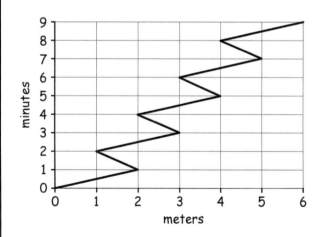

Acting it Out or Using Concrete Material

PROBLEM 46

There is 1½ litres of soup in the jug.

$$2 - 1 + \frac{1}{2} = 1\frac{1}{2}$$

PROBLEM 47

The ladder had 13 rungs.

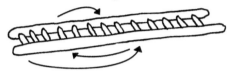

PROBLEM 48

There are 26 trees left (7 are eaten).

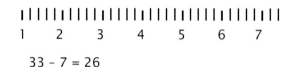

$$33 - 7 = 26$$

PROBLEM 49

Yes, she is correct.

Amount to measure (litres)	How to do it
1	Fill the 3 litre container then use it to fill the 2 litre container, leaving one litre.
2	Use the 2 litre container.
3	Use the 3 litre container.
4	Fill the 2 litre container and pour this into the 3 litre container, then fill the 2 litre container again, giving 4 litres in total.
5	Fill both containers.

PROBLEM 50

The big Vump ate 8 nuts, the medium Vump ate 6 nuts and the little Vump ate 5 nuts.

PROBLEM 51

The journeys proceed as follows (Narf, Narf, Spligg, Spligg in the house to begin with):

Remaining in the house		Flying in the jetcopter		On the safe mountain
NN	→	SS	→	SS
NNS	←	S	←	S
NS	→	N	→	NS
NSS	←	S	←	N
N	→	SS	→	NSS
NS	←	S	←	NS
S	→	N	→	NNS
SS	←	S	←	NN
	→	SS	→	NNSS

PROBLEM 52

There are 5 different rectangles which can be made:

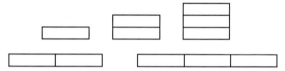

PROBLEM 53

The Tazzle lost one yit.

Transaction	Profit/loss (yits)	Total profit/loss (yits)
Bought two hats	−24	−24
Sold first hat	+18	−6
Sold second hat	+10	+4
Bought back first hat	−11	−7
Sold first hat again	+6	−1

PROBLEM 54

First bag: 3 bricks
Second bag: 24 bricks
Third bag: 13 bricks

Guessing and Checking

Teaching Notes
Guessing and Checking

Guessing and checking is a highly useful strategy for problem solving which is often underestimated. It is a technique that requires pupils to begin with an educated guess (as opposed to a wild guess). The pupil's initial guess should take into account the important aspects of the specific problem. The pupil then checks their guess against the conditions of the problem and, if it is not a correct solution, revises it according to whether it is too small or too large. The process is repeated until a solution is found.

It is very important for pupils using this strategy to first note all of the important facts in the problem. This ensures that their guess is an informed guess, not simply a blind one.

Teachers will need to guide their pupils if their starting points are completely unrealistic. The beginning point for pupils is learning how to make a reasonable guess to begin with. However, pupils will still learn from making faulty guesses.

The best way to deal with the information gathered when using the guess and check method is to draw up a table. This ensures that all guesses and their results are recorded systematically.

The guessing and checking strategy can be used by teachers to encourage those pupils who are not confident in their problem solving ability. It can also be useful when pupils have had limited experience with problem solving, or when they encounter problems that seem to bear little relationship to problems they have solved previously. The following steps are important when guessing and checking to solve a problem.

TAKING NOTE OF THE IMPORTANT FACTS

As mentioned, pupils should begin by taking careful note of the important aspects of the problem and of what is the exact problem they are trying to solve.

For example, consider this problem: Together, Anibob and her sister Plock have 14 toys. Plock has eight more than Anibob. How many toys does each one have?

Pupils should first note the important information given to them in the setting of the problem. In this problem, the important information is that:

Plock has eight more toys than Anibob.
Plock's toys plus Anibob's toys total 14.

What they are trying to find out by solving the problem is the number of toys Plock and Anibob have each.

FINDING A STARTING POINT

The pupil should now make an initial guess and consider whether it is reasonable. In the sample problem, for example, it would not be reasonable to guess that either of them have more than 14 toys, as this is the total number of toys they have between them – the total for the entire problem.

Say the pupil decides that Plock has 10 toys and Anibob has 2.

The best way to keep a systematic record of guesses and results is in a table.

DRAWING UP A TABLE

When drawing up the table, pupils will need to refer to the important factors of the specific problem. For the sample problem, the table should be drawn up with columns for Plock's toys, Anibob's toys and for the total created by adding Plock's toys to Anibob's toys.

Guess	Plock's toys	Anibob's toys	Total

Guessing and Checking

TESTING THE GUESS

Pupils should now test their guess. If Plock has 10 toys and Anibob has 2, the combined total of their toys is 12. Since the required total is 14, this guess is too low.

Guess	Plock's toys	Anibob's toys	Total
1	8	4	12

TOO LOW

The pupils must revise their guess to give a larger total.

Say the pupil now guesses that Plock has 12 toys and Anibob has 4.

Guess	Plock's toys	Anibob's toys	Total
1	10	2	12
2	12	4	16

TOO HIGH

The total is now too high, so the guess needs to be revised to give a smaller total.

If the pupil now guesses that Plock has 11 toys and Anibob has 3, they will find that they have a solution to the problem.

Guess	Plock's toys	Anibob's toys	Total
1	10	2	12
2	12	4	16
3	11	3	14

CORRECT

Because the results have been recorded in the table, pupils can see exactly what guesses they have made and how close to solving the problem it got them.

Guessing and Checking

EXAMPLE 1

Find two consecutive numbers that add up to 27.

Understanding the problem

What do we know?

That we must find two consecutive numbers. The two numbers must total 27.

What do we need to find out?

Questioning:

What are consecutive numbers? Can you give me some examples of consecutive numbers under 10? Can you think of two consecutive numbers over 100? What are three consecutive numbers between 40 and 50?

Planning and communicating a solution

What we did

This is a straightforward problem, which needs to start with a guess. Some pupils will work out right away that the two numbers must be quite close to half of 27. Draw up a table to keep a record of the guesses.

Guess	1st no.	2nd no.	Total
1	11	12	23

The first two consecutive numbers in the first guess were too low so they should be increased.

Guess	1st no.	2nd no.	Total
1	11	12	23
2	14	15	29

Guess two was too high but the total was very close to 27. The solution should now be obvious:

Guess	1st no.	2nd no.	Total
1	11	12	23
2	14	15	29
3	13	14	27

Reflecting and generalising

This problem will be solved mentally by some children but, for others, the guessing and checking strategy provides a useful structure and a tool with which they can find the solution to this type of problem. Talk about the different ways that the problem can be solved and see if they work for other pairs of consecutive numbers.

Extension

This problem is very easy to extend by either increasing the size of the numbers or by asking pupils to find three consecutive numbers. For example, which two consecutive numbers add up to 121? Which three consecutive numbers add up to 36?

Guessing and Checking

EXAMPLE 2

In the sticker shop, round stickers cost 5p and square ones cost 4p. If a group spent 31p in the shop, how many of each sticker did they buy?

Understanding the problem

What do we know?
Round stickers cost 5p.
Square stickers cost 4p.
31p was spent altogether.

What do we need to find out?
Questioning:
How many round and square stickers were bought? Was the money spent on just one type?

Planning and communicating a solution

What we did
Begin by making a guess at the number of each type of sticker bought. With a problem like this, involving both quantities and money, it is essential to keep a careful record of each guess and result, so draw up a table.

Guess	Number of round stickers	Number of square stickers	Total cost
1	2 (10p)	3 (12p)	22p

The first guess was too low, so the next step is to increase the numbers of stickers. Notice how the money spent is recorded in brackets.

Guess	Number of round stickers	Number of square stickers	Total cost
1	2 (10p)	3 (12p)	22p
2	3 (15p)	6 (24p)	39p

The second guess was too high but it produced a total in the thirties, so guess three should be close to guess two. The table below shows how the correct answer was reached by guess 4.

Guess	Number of round stickers	Number of square stickers	Total cost
1	2 (10p)	3 (12p)	22p
2	3 (15p)	6 (24p)	39p
3	3 (15p)	5 (20p)	35p
4	3 (15p)	4 (16p)	31p

Reflecting and generalising

Discuss the problem with pupils. Why did there have to be an odd number of round stickers? Why could the answer not have included five round stickers. Could the problem have been solved a different way?

Extension

The number of stickers could be increased and the total spent raised, or each sticker could be made more expensive to extend the mental calculation required.

Guessing and Checking

EXAMPLE 3

A Woon spent Monday and Tuesday spotting snakes. He spotted 24 snakes altogether. If he saw three times as many on Tuesday as he did on Monday, how many snakes did he spot each day?

Understanding the problem

What do we know?
The Woon saw 24 snakes over 2 days.
He saw some on Monday and 3 times more on Tuesday.

What do we need to find out?
Questioning:
How many snakes did he see each day?
Will guessing and checking be helpful?

Planning and communicating a solution

What we did
Begin by making a guess at the number of snakes spotted on Monday then calculating how many were spotted on Tuesday. Once more, a simple table helps to clarify what is going on.

Guess	Snakes seen on Monday	Snakes seen on Tuesday	Total
1	10	30	40

The first guess was too high, so the next step is to come up with a lower number.

Guess	Snakes seen on Monday	Snakes seen on Tuesday	Total
1	10	30	40
2	5	15	20

The second guess was too low but produced a total quite close to the target number of 24. Encourage pupils to look out for clues like this: if 5 (snakes seen on Monday) gave a close answer, then the correct solution must be near 5.

Guess	Snakes seen on Monday	Snakes seen on Tuesday	Total
1	10	30	40
2	5	15	20
3	6	18	24

Reflecting and generalising

As always, we should encourage pupils to find other ways of solving problems, so talk about different approaches which might also work. Also, look for patterns in the table to help pupils with their understanding of the mathematics of the problem.

Extension

The problem could be extended by including three days of successive increase or the factor of increase could be extended. Addition or subtraction could also be used instead of multiplication.

Guessing and Checking

★ **Understanding the problem**

List what you know.

. . . .

. . . .

. . . .

★ **What do you need to find out?**

Is there anything you don't understand?
What are you being asked to find out?

. . . .

. . . .

. . . .

. . . .

★ **Finding and writing the answer**

Is your guess reasonable?
Can your guess be raised or lowered?
Are you working carefully in a pattern or order?

. . . .

. . . .

. . . .

. . . .

★ **Thinking about the problem**

What did you find?
Did you check your answer to see if it matched the question?
Was there another way you could have done it?

. . . .

. . . .

. . . .

. . . .

PROBLEM 55 | Numbers 12₃ |

Level A

Which 3 of these numbers add up to 20?

1, 8, 5, 10, 7

PROBLEM 56 | Numbers 12₃ |

Level A

Globbi is 4 years older than Smuk. Their ages added together total 18. How old are they?

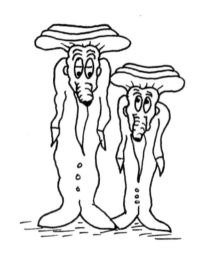

PROBLEM 57 | Numbers 12₃ |

Level A

Find two consecutive numbers that add up to 23.

PROBLEM 58 | Numbers 123

Level A

Booj has 20 socks. She has 10 more green ones than blue ones. How many green socks does she have?

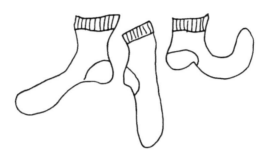

PROBLEM 59 | Numbers 123

Level A

10 aliens visit the seaside. There are 4 more children than adults. How many adults are there?

PROBLEM 60 | Numbers 123

Level A

Rup has twice as many pieces of cheese as Mebo. If they have 9 pieces of cheese altogether, how many does each have?

PROBLEM 61   Numbers 1 2 3

Level
B

Qeb scored 6 more goals than his brother, Zerl, in a tentacleball match. If they scored 40 goals in total, how many did each brother score?

PROBLEM 62   Numbers 1 2 3

Level
B

Find two consecutive numbers that add up to 133.

PROBLEM 63   Numbers 1 2 3

Level
B

On Venus, ants have 8 legs and caterpillars have just 3. If there were 26 legs on a leaf, how many ants and caterpillars were on the leaf?

PROBLEM 64 · Numbers 123 · Level B

Yemmo bought 21 magazines over a 3 day period. Each day she bought 3 more magazines than the day before. How many magazines did she buy on the first day?

PROBLEM 65 · Numbers 123 · Level B

Complete the following triangle with the numbers 2, 3, 4, 5, 6, 7. Each side must add up to 12.

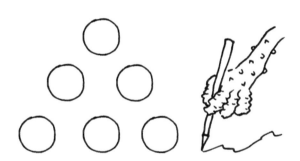

PROBLEM 66 · Numbers 123 · Level B

Find 3 odd numbers over 10 with a sum of 49.

PROBLEM 67 | Measures

Level C

2 friends from the planet Vock cycled 100km over 4 days. They got very tired and each day cycled 10km less than the previous day. How far did they cycle on the first day?

PROBLEM 68 | Measures

Level C

On Saturn, lollies cost 6 nittles and ice creams cost 7 nittles. If a family spent 33 nittles on lollies and ice creams, how many of each did they buy?

PROBLEM 69 | Numbers 123

Level C

Find 3 consecutive numbers that add up to 57.

PROBLEM 70 Numbers 12₃

Level C

Grank is half as old as Oxxi but twice as old as Smoof. If the sum of their ages is 28, how old is Grank?

PROBLEM 71 Measures

Level C

On the planet Kikiki they accept Earth money. A lemonade and a bun costs £1.80.

If the bun costs twice as much as the lemonade, what is the price of each one?

PROBLEM 72 Numbers 12₃

Level C

A Scobble has 34 eyes, noses and mouths altogether. It has 3 more noses than eyes, and 4 more mouths than noses. How many eyes, mouths and noses does a Scobble have?

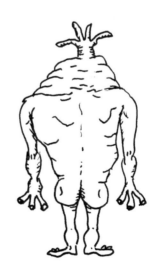

Guessing and checking

PROBLEM 55

$8 + 5 + 7 = 20$

PROBLEM 56

Sample guess and check solution:

Guess	Globbi	Smuk	Total	
1	9	5	14	too low
2	12	8	20	too high
3	11	7	18	correct

Globbi is 11 and Smuk is 7.

PROBLEM 57

Sample guess and check solution:
Guess 1: $10 + 11 = 21$ too low
Guess 2: $11 + 12 = 23$ correct

The two consecutive numbers are 11 and 12.

PROBLEM 58

Sample guess and check solution:

Guess	Blue	Green	Total	
1	9	19	28	too high
2	7	17	24	too high
3	4	14	18	too low
4	5	15	20	correct

Booj has 5 blue and 15 green socks.

PROBLEM 59

Sample guess and check solution:

Guess	Adults	Children	Total	
1	2	6	8	too low
2	4	8	12	too high
3	3	7	10	correct

There are 3 adults at the seaside.

PROBLEM 60

Sample guess and check solution:

Guess	Mebo	Rup	Total	
1	5	10	15	too high
2	2	4	6	too low
3	3	6	9	correct

Rup has 6 pieces of cheese and Mebo has 3.

PROBLEM 61

Sample guess and check solution:

Guess	Zerl	Qeb	Total	
1	10	16	26	too low
2	15	21	36	too low
3	20	26	46	too high
4	17	23	40	correct

Qeb scored 23 goals and Zerl scored 17.

PROBLEM 62

Sample guess and check solution:
Guess 1: $62 + 63 = 125$ too low
Guess 2: $71 + 72 = 143$ too high
Guess 3: $67 + 68 = 135$ too high
Guess 4: $66 + 67 = 133$ correct

The 2 consecutive numbers are 66 and 67.

PROBLEM 63

Sample guess and check solution:

Guess	Ants	Caterpillars	Total legs	
1	2 (16 legs)	3 (9 legs)	25	too low
2	2 (16 legs)	4 (12 legs)	28	too high
3	1 (8 legs)	6 (18 legs)	26	correct

1 ant and 6 caterpillars are on the leaf.

Guessing and checking

PROBLEM 64

Sample guess and check solution:

	Day 1	Day 2	Day 3	Total	
1	8	11	14	33	too high
2	5	8	11	24	too high
3	4	7	10	21	correct

Yemmo bought 4 magazines on the first day.

PROBLEM 65

Possible solutions:

```
      2              2              3
   7  6          6  7          5  7
  3  5  4       4  5  3       4  6  2

      3              4              4
   7  5          5  6          6  5
  2  6  4       3  7  2       2  7  3
```

In each case, the corner numbers are 2, 3, 4.

PROBLEM 66

There are many possible solutions, including:

```
13, 15, 21    11, 15, 23
11, 11, 27    13, 17, 19
```

PROBLEM 67

Sample guess and check solution:

	Day 1	Day 2	Day 3	Day 4	Total	
1	60	50	40	30	180	too high
2	30	20	10	0	60	too low
3	40	30	20	10	100	correct

They cycled 40km on the first day.

PROBLEM 68

Sample guess and check solution:

Guess	Lollies	Ice creams	Total cost	
1	4 (24n)	1 (7n)	31n	too low
2	3 (18n)	2 (14n)	32n	too low
3	2 (12n)	4 (28n)	40n	too high
4	2 (12n)	3 (21n)	33n	correct

They bought 2 lollies and 3 ice creams.

PROBLEM 69

Sample guess and check solution:
Guess 1: 16 + 17 + 18 = 51 too low
Guess 2: 19 + 20 + 21 = 60 too high
Guess 3: 18 + 19 + 20 = 57 correct

PROBLEM 70

Sample guess and check solution:

	Smoof	Grank	Oxxi	Total	
1	6	12	24	42	too high
2	3	6	12	21	too low
3	4	8	16	28	correct

Grank is 8 years old.

PROBLEM 71

Sample guess and check solution:

Guess	Lemonade	Bun	Total	
1	40p	80p	£1.20	too low
2	50p	£1	£1.50	too low
3	60p	£1.20	£1.80	correct

Lemonade costs 60p and a bun costs £1.20.

PROBLEM 72

Sample guess and check solution:

	Eyes	Noses	Mouths	Total	
1	2	5	9	16	too low
2	6	9	13	28	too low
3	10	13	17	40	too high
4	8	11	15	34	correct

A Scobble has 8 eyes, 11 noses and 15 mouths.

Creating an Organised List

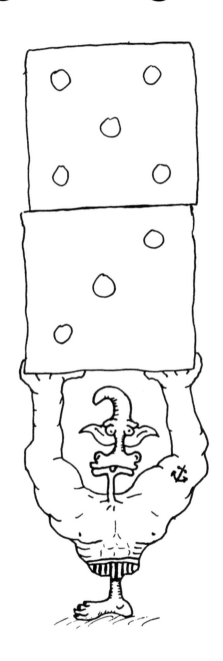

Solve
THAT PROBLEM!

Solve
THAT PROBLEM!

Solve
THAT PROBLEM!

Creating an Organised List

This strategy is similar to *Drawing a Table* (see page 19) but is normally used when there is a greater amount of information to be set out in a more systematic fashion, so that probable solutions can be clearly seen. Pupils need to follow a procedure or sequence to ensure that all possibilities are listed and to prevent repetition.

When creating a list, one item should be kept the same or constant while others change. The one that is kept constant should be examined to see if it has different values or components that can be listed.

Pupils should get into the habit of writing down the process they are using.

The following skills should be developed when working with this strategy.

Work sequentially

Decide on a starting point then work methodically.

Example: Kron is buying fruit for his tea. There are four different types of fruit in the shop, but he can only afford two. How many choices does he have?

Give each fruit a letter: A, B, C, D.

AA	BB	CC	DD
AB	BC	CD	
AC	BD		
AD			

Ten choices can be made.

Filling in the gaps after working out a pattern

This skill challenges pupils to visualise and create imaginative pictures. The results are then listed.

For example: Three monsters called Yerg, Fump and Scrid are going on a car journey.

One must drive and one must read the map. How many different possibilities are there for the driver and map reader?

Driver	Map Reader
Yerg	Fump
	Scrid

For each driver there are two possible map readers.

The answer is 3 x 2 = 6.

Combinations of numbers

At times, pupils are given problems that ask them to combine a series of numbers.

Example: Immi has to buy three presents for her teachers. There are vases for £2, candles for £1 and books for £4. What amounts could she spend?

Pupils will need to work systematically. They should start by listing all the possible combinations using £1.

1 + 1 + 1 = 3	2 + 1 + 1 = 4
1 + 1 + 2 = 4	2 + 1 + 2 = 5
1 + 1 + 4 = 6	2 + 1 + 4 = 7
1 + 2 + 1 = 4	2 + 2 + 1 = 5
1 + 2 + 2 = 5	2 + 2 + 2 = 6
1 + 2 + 4 = 7	2 + 2 + 4 = 8
1 + 4 + 1 = 6	2 + 4 + 1 = 7
1 + 4 + 2 = 7	2 + 4 + 2 = 8
1 + 4 + 4 = 9	2 + 4 + 4 = 10

4 + 1 + 1 = 6
4 + 1 + 2 = 7
4 + 1 + 4 = 9
4 + 2 + 1 = 7
4 + 2 + 2 = 8
4 + 2 + 4 = 10
4 + 4 + 1 = 9
4 + 4 + 2 = 10
4 + 4 + 4 = 12

Notice that some answers are the same. Only the different amounts are required, not all of them. The possible answers are: £3, £4, £5, £6, £7, £8, £9, £10 and £12.

Creating an Organised List

EXAMPLE 1

Every day, Jullu has to clean his teeth, wash his hair and trim his claws. He likes to do them in a different order each day. How many different ways can he do this?

Understanding the problem

What do we know?
That Jullu has three things to do.
That they can be done in any order.

What do we need to find out?
Questioning:
How many different ways can he do the three things? Can he start with the same task more than once?

Planning and communicating a solution

What we did
Approach the list systematically. Start with cleaning teeth and then place the other two tasks in their possible positions.

T H C
T C H
H T C
H C T
C T H
C H T

There are six different possibilities.

Reflecting and generalising

The key to avoiding the omission of one of the possibilities is to follow a system of careful ordering, as above. Begin with the first task mentioned, then move to the second task mentioned, each time listing all the permutations.

Extension

A similar approach can be tried using four tasks.

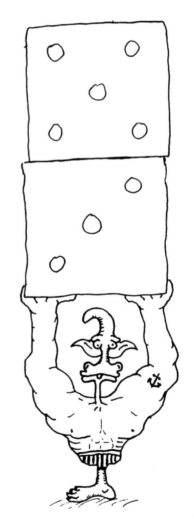

Creating an Organised List

EXAMPLE 2

If five monsters go to a party and each monster dances with each of the other monsters, how many dances are there in total?

Understanding the problem

What do we know?
That there are five monsters.
That each one dances with all of the others.

What do we need to find out?
Questioning:
How many partners will each monster dance with? How many dances will there be altogether?

Planning and communicating a solution

What we did
Call the first monster M1, the second M2 and so on. Begin by listing who M1 has to dance with.

M1 dances with M2.
M1 dances with M3.
M1 dances with M4.
M1 dances with M5.

Next, list who M2 dances with, bearing in mind that the M1-M2 dance is already listed.

M2 dances with M3.
M2 dances with M4.
M2 dances with M5.

Continue for M3 then the others:

M3 dances with M4.
M3 dances with M5.

M4 dances with M5.

All of M5's four dances are already listed so, counting up, we can see that the total is 10.

Reflecting and generalising

Some pupils may have expected that the solution to the problem would have been 5 x 4 = 20 as there are five monsters and each dances with the other four. By being systematic and listing each monster in turn, we can ensure that errors like this are avoided.

Extension

The number of monsters dancing could be increased.

Creating an Organised List

EXAMPLE 3

How many ways can you roll a total score of seven with two dice?

Understanding the problem

What do we know?
Two dice are rolled.
A total of seven must be scored.

What do we need to find out?
Questioning:
How can seven be scored with two dice?
How many different ways is this possible?

Planning and communicating a solution

What we did
List all the possible score combinations that total seven. Again, the key here is to be systematic about the way the list is constructed, so that no valid combinations are missed.

Start with the lowest score on the first die and work up:

    1 and 6
    2 and 5
    3 and 4
    4 and 3
    5 and 2
    6 and 1

There are six ways altogether to throw a combination that adds up to seven.

Reflecting and generalising

Ask if there are other ways to solve this problem. Can the list be constructed differently? Why is it important to list the numbers in order? Discuss the patterns that appear in the list.

Extension

Find out how many ways other totals can be thrown. How many ways can ten be thrown with three dice? How many ways can a score of ten be thrown with ten dice? What is the highest score that can be thrown with a given number of dice?

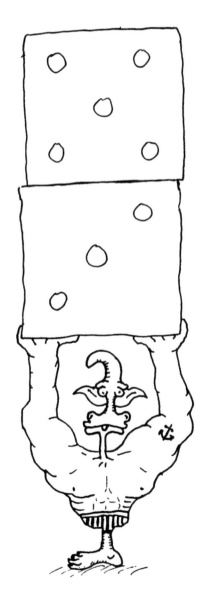

CREATING AN ORGANISED LIST

★ **Understanding the problem**
List what you know.

. . . .

. . . .

. . . .

. . . .

★ **What do you need to find out?**
Is there anything you don't understand?
What are you being asked to find out?

. . . .

. . . .

. . . .

. . . .

★ **Finding and writing the answer**
Are you working in a sequence?
Can you develop a pattern?

. . . .

. . . .

. . . .

. . . .

★ **Thinking about the problem**
What did you find?
Did you check your answer to see if it matched the question?
Was there another way you could have done it?

. . . .

. . . .

. . . .

. . . .

PROBLEM 73   Shape & Space

Level **A**

Apples on Xooi are dotty, lumpy or striped. How many different ways can the 3 apples be arranged in a line?

PROBLEM 74   Numbers 123

Level **A**

How many different totals can be rolled with 2 dice?

PROBLEM 75   Numbers 123

Level **A**

Toggis love to wear odd shoes on their 2 feet. If a Toggi has a yellow left shoe and a blue left shoe, plus a red right shoe and a white right shoe, how many different pairs can she wear?

PROBLEM 76 Numbers 1 2 3

Level A

4 Doffs meet at a party and each gives all the others a hug. How many hugs will there be altogether?

PROBLEM 77 Numbers 1 2 3

Level A

A Ximp drops 2 photos. They can either land face up or face down. How many different outcomes are possible?

PROBLEM 78 Numbers 1 2 3

Level A

The ages of 3 very young aliens add up to 6. If each is at least a year old, what could their ages be?

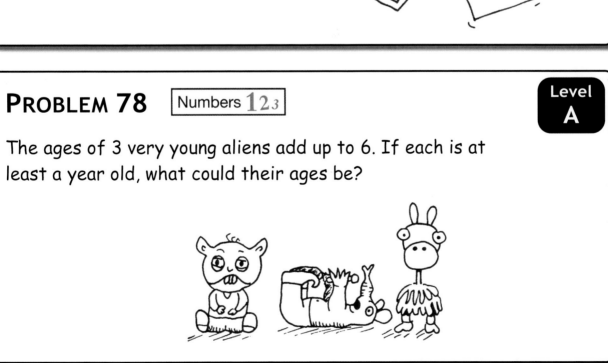

PROBLEM 79 Numbers 123

How many different totals can be rolled with 3 dice?

Level B

PROBLEM 80 Numbers 123

Ayu wants to paint the front door and the back door of his house each a different colour. He has five colours to choose from. How many combinations are possible?

Level B

PROBLEM 81 Numbers 123

In a café, Kloob can have apple or plum crumble with a topping of either cream, custard or ice cream. How many different choices are there?

Level B

PROBLEM 82 Numbers 1 2 3

Level **B**

A family of 5 Phrots exchange presents on New Year's Day. If Phrots only give presents to members of the family older than themselves, how many presents will be given?

PROBLEM 83 Numbers 1 2 3

Level **B**

A Yeem has to make sandwiches with 2 different fillings. The choices are ham, pickle, cheese, egg, lettuce and tomato. How many different sandwiches are possible?

PROBLEM 84 Numbers 1 2 3

Level **B**

If 3 coins are tossed, how many different outcomes are possible?

PROBLEM 85 — Numbers 123

Level C

There are 6 aliens in Smad's family. When they go to a fun fair, their rollercoaster car has 2 rows of 3 seats. The 3 oldest must sit in the front seats and the 3 youngest in the back seats. How many different ways are there for the 6 members of Smad's family to sit in the car?

PROBLEM 86 — Numbers 123

Level C

Nozziland on the planet Perg is designing a new flag with the design shown here. They want to use blue, red, green and pink. How many different ways can the colours be arranged?

PROBLEM 87 — Numbers 123

Level C

Urpl is allowed to buy 2 sweets from a shop. The shop has 4 different sweets, costing 2 zibs, 5 zibs, 6 zibs and 9 zibs each. What possible amounts could Urpl spend on the 2 sweets?

Creating an Organised List

PROBLEM 73

There are 6 ways to arrange the apples:

D L S
D S L
L D S
L S D
S D L
S L D

PROBLEM 74

1 + 1 = 2 lowest
6 + 6 = 12 highest

All totals in between can be rolled, so there are 11 in total.

PROBLEM 75

YR   YW
BR   BW

There are 4 different pairs she can wear.

PROBLEM 76

D1 hugs D2
D1 hugs D3
D1 hugs D4
D2 hugs D3
D2 hugs D4
D3 hugs D4

There are 6 hugs in total.

PROBLEM 77

UU
UD
DU
DD

There are 4 possible combinations.

PROBLEM 78

The 3 ages could be any of the following combinations:

1, 1, 4
1, 2, 3
2, 2, 2

PROBLEM 79

1 + 1 + 1 = 3 lowest
6 + 6 + 6 = 18 highest

All totals in between can be rolled, so there are 16 in total.

PROBLEM 80

For front door colour A, the back door colour could be B, C, D, E.

There are five possible front door colours, so 5 x 4 = 20.

There are 20 different combinations possible.

PROBLEM 81

With Apple Crumble:
    Cream
    Custard
    Ice cream

With Plum Crumble:
    Cream
    Custard
    Ice cream

There are 6 different choices.

Creating an Organised List

PROBLEM 82

Call the oldest member of the family A and the youngest E.

A gives 0 presents
B gives 1
C gives 2
D gives 3
E gives 4

$1 + 2 + 3 + 4 = 10$

10 presents will be given in total.

PROBLEM 83

ham & pickle
ham & cheese
ham & egg
ham & lettuce
ham & tomato
pickle & cheese
pickle & egg
pickle & lettuce
pickle & tomato
cheese & egg
cheese & lettuce
cheese & tomato
egg & lettuce
egg & tomato
lettuce & tomato

There are 15 different sandwiches possible.

PROBLEM 84

HHH	TTT
HHT	TTH
HTH	THT
HTT	THH

8 outcomes are possible.

PROBLEM 85

Number the 3 oldest 1, 2, 3.
Number the 3 youngest 4, 5, 6.

Possible front seat positions:

123
132
213
231
312
321

For each of these, there are six ways that the three youngest aliens can be seated.

$6 \times 6 = 36$.

There are 36 different ways the family can be seated.

PROBLEM 86

Arranging the colours left, top, bottom, right, starting with blue on the left:

BRGP
BRPG
BGRP
BGPR
BPRG
BPGR

Placing each of the colours on the left gives 6 combinations.

$4 \times 6 = 24$

There are 24 different designs possible.

PROBLEM 87

Listing all the combinations:

$2 + 2 = 4$ $5 + 2 = 7$ $6 + 2 = 8$ $9 + 2 = 11$
$2 + 5 = 7$ $5 + 5 = 10$ $6 + 5 = 11$ $9 + 5 = 14$
$2 + 6 = 8$ $5 + 6 = 11$ $6 + 6 = 12$ $9 + 6 = 15$
$2 + 9 = 11$ $5 + 9 = 14$ $6 + 9 = 15$ $9 + 9 = 18$

The possible totals are 4, 7, 8, 10, 11, 12, 14, 15, 18.

Looking for a Pattern

Solve
THAT PROBLEM!

Solve
THAT PROBLEM!

Solve
THAT PROBLEM!

Looking for a Pattern

This strategy is an extension to *Drawing a Table* and *Creating an Organised List* (see page 19 and page 64). It is one of the most frequently used problem solving strategies, as mathematical patterns can be found everywhere – in nature, numbers and in shapes. Pupils learn through probability and prediction to distinguish between different patterns.

When a pattern is established, it is easy to predict what comes next. The most common way to check if there is a pattern is to:

* Find the difference between two consecutive numbers.
* Decide whether the numbers have been multiplied or divided by any given number.
* Find out if they are rising or falling numbers that increase or decrease following a regular sequence.

Once a pupil recognises a pattern, it can be extended or continued.

It is important for pupils to realise that a lot of the problem solving skills they learn build on or are connected to one another.

The following skills and strategies need to be developed by pupils to help them solve problems that involve looking for a pattern.

Creating and continuing a pattern

Ask pupils to complete the following three number patterns. There is more than one possible answer.

Example: 3   5   8   ___   ___

Some possible patterns are:				
a)	3 5 8	12	17	
b)	3 5 8	10	13	
c)	3 5 8	3	5	
d)	3 5 8	13	21	

They are all correct, as each has established its own pattern based on the first three numbers and each pattern can be explained.

In a), the difference between the numbers increases by one each time. First it is 2, then 3, then 4, etc.

In b), the difference between the first two numbers and the second two numbers increases by one, and then this +2, +3 pattern is repeated.

In c), the initial pattern is begun again and repeated.

In d), the previous two numbers are added to make the next number.

For problems similar to the above example, it is important for pupils to see that it is possible to have more than one correct answer, if the patterns created can be explained. A calculator can be a helpful tool to use when looking at patterns.

Spatial patterns

To help pupils explore spatially, give them a set pattern series.

* On the first line, draw a row of three triangular flags with a pattern in each: a single solid horizontal line in the first, a single dotted oblique line in the second and a single dot in the third.
* On the second line, draw a row of three rectangular flags with a pattern in each: two solid horizontal lines in the first, two dotted oblique lines in the second and two dots in the third.
* On the third line, draw a row of three rounded flags with a pattern in each: three solid horizontal lines in the first, three dotted oblique lines in the second and three dots in the third.
* A definite pattern has been established.

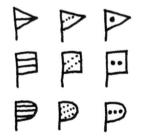

Pupils can continue their exploration of the pattern. They can add new shapes or explore new patterns using the three shapes already provided.

Looking for a Pattern

FINDING A PATTERN IN A TABLE

Before looking for a pattern, pupils need to go through the process of creating a table. They need to decide: Are there one, two, three or more variables? Is a 'total' column necessary?

Example: Three out of every four garden tools made in a factory is a spade. If there are 20 garden tools made, how many will be spades?

Draw up a table with three columns headed 'Spades', 'Other tools' and 'Total tools':

Spades	Other tools	Total tools
1	3	4
2	6	8
3	9	12
4	12	16
5	15	20

We can see that a pattern has been established. The 'Spades' column is increasing in ones, and the 'Other tools' in multiples of three. So, if there is a total of 20 tools made, five will be spades and 15 will be other tools.

Looking for a Pattern

EXAMPLE 1

The supermarket is building a display of cans, following the pattern below. How many cans are needed if the display is to be six cans high?

Understanding the problem

What do we know?

The cans are stacked in a triangle pattern. The number of cans increases as the height of the display increases.

What do we need to find out?

Questioning:

How many cans are needed if the display is to be six cans high? How many cans are needed for a display one can high? Two cans high? Is there a pattern?

Planning and communicating a solution

What we did

A table is needed so that the number of cans can be recorded and a pattern found. To help pupils, a drawing can be made using dots to represent the cans. The two variables are the height of the display and the number of cans.

Height	Total cans
1	1
2	3
3	6
4	10
5	15
6	21

21 cans are needed for a display six cans high.

Reflecting and generalising

The table shows that the total number of cans follows the pattern of triangular numbers. The number of cans added increases by one for each increase in height.

Extension

Greater heights can be explored. Pupils could also be asked to find the height of a display containing a particular number of cans.

Looking for a Pattern

EXAMPLE 2

A Scork collects shells during his holiday. Starting on Monday, he collects three shells. The next day he collects four shells then, the day after that, five shells. If he continues this pattern, how many shells will he have by the end of the following Monday?

Understanding the problem

What do we know?
The Scork starts with three shells.
The number of shells collected increases by one each day.

What do we need to find out?
Questioning:
How many shells will the Scork have by the end of the following Monday? How can we record the pattern?

Planning and communicating a solution

What we did
Pupils should draw up a table so that the pattern can clearly be seen. The first two columns record the days and the number of shells collected on each day. A total column will show the overall number of shells.

Day	Shells collected	Total
Mon	3	3
Tues	4	7
Wed	5	12
Thur	6	18
Fri	7	25
Sat	8	33
Sun	9	42
Mon	10	52

The Scork collected 52 shells by the end of the following Monday.

Reflecting and generalising

This problem would have been very difficult to solve without a table, despite the very simple pattern in the second column.

Extension

The increase could be extended to two or three more shells per day. Pupils could be asked to find how many shells were collected on the day when a particular total is reached.

Looking for a Pattern

EXAMPLE 3

For every two rocks eaten by Blugg, Fimple eats five. How many rocks will Blugg have eaten by the time Fimple has eaten 100?

Understanding the problem

What do we know?
Blugg and Fimple eat rocks.
Blugg eats two rocks for every five eaten by Fimple.

What do we need to find out?
Questioning:
How many rocks will Blugg have eaten when Fimple eats 100? How can we record the pattern?

Planning and communicating a solution
What we did
Draw up a table with two columns. The first column records rocks eaten by Blugg and the second rocks eaten by Fimple.

Rocks eaten by Blugg	Rocks eaten by Fimple
2	5
4	10
6	15
8	20
10	25
12	30
14	35
16	40
18	45
20	50

We can extend the table up to 100 rocks but pupils should be able to see the patterns and use them to calculate that Blugg will have eaten 40 rocks by the time Fimple has eaten 100.

Reflecting and generalising

The first column showing Glubb's rocks has a simple increase in twos while Fimple's column increases in fives. By extending the two patterns, we can complete the table and work with larger numbers.

Extension

Different numbers can be used to make the patterns more challenging. Pupils could also be asked to extend the patterns even further.

Looking for a Pattern

★ **Understanding the problem**
List what you know.

....

....

....

★ **What do you need to find out?**
Is there anything you don't understand?
What are you being asked to find out?

....

....

....

....

★ **Finding and writing the answer**
Are you working in a sequence?
Can you find a pattern?
Can you continue the pattern?

....

....

....

....

★ **Thinking about the problem**
What did you find?
Did you check your answer to see if it matched the question?
Was there another way you could have done it?

....

....

....

....

PROBLEM 88 | Shape & Space

Level A

Urgl has set her sister a puzzle. She has to draw the next shape in this pattern. Can you draw it?

PROBLEM 89 | Numbers 1 2 3

Level A

Each of these groups of numbers follows a pattern.
Find the pattern and write down the next 3 numbers:

a) 3   5   7   9   ___   ___   ___

b) 1   1½   2   2½   ___   ___   ___

c) 14   12   10   8   ___   ___   ___

d) 75   70   65   60   ___   ___   ___

PROBLEM 90 | Shape & Space

Level A

Here is a repeating pattern using 3 shapes. Can you make a different one using the same shapes?

✳ ✳ ☐ ☐ ○ ○ ✳ ✳ ☐ ☐ ○ ○

PROBLEM 91 · Shape & Space

Level A

Look for a pattern in this row of triangles. Fill in the last 2 triangles to finish the pattern.

PROBLEM 92 · Numbers 1 2 3

Level A

What is the next number in this sequence?

8	8	9	9	10	

PROBLEM 93 · Numbers 1 2 3

Level A

What is the same about these 2 patterns?

5	4	5	4	5	4
10	11	10	11	10	11

PROBLEM 94 | Numbers 1 2 3

Level B

Each of these groups of numbers follows a pattern.
Find each pattern and write down the next 3 numbers.

a) 24   35   46   57   ___   ___   ___

b) 1   10   100   1000   ___   ___   ___

c) 22   21   19   16   ___   ___   ___

d) 5   9   10   14   ___   ___   ___

PROBLEM 95 | Numbers 1 2 3

Level B

An Uffle cut a pile of 5 pieces of paper in half with his laser scissors. He then put the halves into one pile and cut them in half. He did this 4 times. How many pieces of paper did he end up with?

PROBLEM 96 | Shape & Space

Level B

Zym was building some walls following this pattern. How many bricks were in the seventh pattern?

Problem Solving Task Cards
Looking for a Pattern

PROBLEM 97 — Numbers 123 — Level B

Glopp is given 9 stamps. The next day he is given 10 stamps. If he is given 1 more stamp than the previous day each time, how many stamps will he have after 5 days?

PROBLEM 98 — Numbers 123 — Level B

What are the next 2 numbers in this pattern?

| 10 | 16 | 20 | 13 | 30 | 10 | | |

PROBLEM 99 — Numbers 123 — Level B

On the first day of his holidays, Preed has 18 vouchers. He spends 3 vouchers the next day and every day after that. On what day will he have 6 vouchers left?

PROBLEM 100 | Numbers 1 2 3

Level C

Moof loves buying cacti. On the first day of May, he buys 2 cacti. On the second day, he also buys 2 cacti. On the third and fourth days, he buys 3 cacti and, on the fifth and sixth days, he buys 4. On which days will he buy 7 cacti?

PROBLEM 101 | Measures

Level C

Thox and Niffa are having a race. For every 6 metres that Thox runs, Niffa runs 5. How far will Thox have run when Niffa has run 40 metres?

PROBLEM 102 | Numbers 1 2 3

Level C

At Org's space helmet show, 1 helmet costs six tiks. 2 helmets cost 11 tiks, 3 helmets cost 16 tiks and 4 cost 21 tiks. How much will 9 helmets cost?

Looking for a Pattern

PROBLEM 88

PROBLEM 89

a) 11, 13, 15 (2 is added each time)
b) 3, 3½, 4 (½ is added each time)
c) 6, 4, 2 (2 is subtracted each time)
d) 55, 50, 45 (5 is subtracted each time)

PROBLEM 90

Teacher to check. Here is one possible answer:

* □ O * □ O * □ O * □ O

PROBLEM 91

The final two triangles should be as follows:

PROBLEM 92

The next number is 10.
The pattern is +0 +1 +0 +1 etc.

PROBLEM 93

In each pattern, one is added then subtracted in sequence.

PROBLEM 94

a) 68, 79, 90 (11 is added each time)
b) 10,000, 100,000, 1,000,000
    (multiply by ten each time)
c) 12, 7, 1 (subtract 1, 2, 3, 4, 5, 6)
d) 15, 19, 20 (add 4 then 1)

PROBLEM 95

Cut	Pieces
0	5
1	10
2	20
3	40
4	80

He ended up with 80 pieces of paper.

PROBLEM 96

The pattern is square numbers:

Wall	Bricks
1	1
2	4
3	9
4	16
5	25
6	36
7	49

There were 49 bricks in the seventh wall.

Looking for a Pattern

PROBLEM 97

Day	Stamps given	Total
1	9	9
2	10	19
3	11	30
4	12	42
5	13	55

He had 55 stamps after 5 days.

PROBLEM 98

The next 2 numbers are 40 and 7.

The numbers in square boxes are increasing by 10. The numbers in the rounded boxes are decreasing by 3.

PROBLEM 99

Day	Vouchers
1	18
2	15
3	12
4	9
5	6

He has 6 vouchers on the fifth day.

PROBLEM 100

Day	Cacti
1	2
2	2
3	3
4	3
5	4
6	4
7	5
8	5
9	6
10	6
11	7
12	7

He will buy 7 on the 11ᵗʰ and 12ᵗʰ days.

PROBLEM 101

Thox	Niffa
6	5
12	10
18	15
24	20
30	25
36	30
42	35
48	40

Thox will have run 48 metres.

PROBLEM 102

Number of helmets	Cost
1	6
2	11
3	16
4	21
5	26
6	31
7	36
8	41
9	46

9 helmets will cost 46 tiks.

2 helmets have a discount of 1 tik, 3 helmets have a discount of 2 tiks, and so on.

This creates the pattern above.

Badger Publishing Limited
15 Wedgwood Gate
Pin Green Industrial Estate
Stevenage, Hertfordshire SG1 4SU
Telephone: 01438 356907
Fax: 01438 747015
www.badger-publishing.co.uk
enquiries@badger-publishing.co.uk

Badger Maths Problem Solving
Year 3

First published 2007
ISBN 978-1-84691-140-8

Andy Seed has created and illustrated an amazing cast of 60 different monsters specially for this book.

Publisher: David Jamieson
Editor: Paul Martin
Designer: Adam Wilmott
Illustrator: Andy Seed

Printed in the UK

For details of the full range of books and resources from

Badger Publishing

including

- **Book Boxes** for Early Years, Infants, Juniors and Special Needs
- **Badger Guided Reading** and book packs for KS1-2
- **Badger Reading Journals** for KS2
- **Badger Nursery Rhymes and Storyteller** – for Early Years and KS1
- **First Facts** – non-fiction for infants
- **Full Flight, Dark Flight, First Flight & Rex Jones** for reluctant readers
- **Brainwaves** – non-fiction to get your brain buzzing
- **Teaching Writing and Writing Poetry** – for Years 1-6
- **Expert at...** *English and Speaking & Listening* – Copymaster books
- **Delbert's Worksheets and Practice Questions** for the KS1-2 Maths SATs
- **Badger Maths: Problem Solving** Books 1-2
- **Badger KS2 Revision Quizzes** for *English*, *Maths* and *Science*
- **Badger Test Revision Guides** for *English*, *Maths* and *Science*
- **SATs Practice Papers** for *English*, *Maths* and *Science*
- **Badger Religious Education** – complete course for the primary school
- **Badger Geography** – complete course for the primary school
- **Badger Science** – complete course for the primary school
- **Badger Comprehension** – complete courses for the primary school
- **Badger ICT** – complete course for the primary school
- **Badger Citizenship & PSHE** – complete course for the primary school
- **Badger French** – simple resources for non-specialist teachers
- **Basic Background Knowledge** – History, Geography
- **Badger History** for KS1 – big books and teacher books
- **Class Act** – easy, inspiring cross-curricular drama for KS2
- **Badger Assembly Stories** – PSHE, RE, Sensitive Issues and Global Issues

- **Interactive Whiteboard CD-ROMs**
Badger Comprehension Interactive
Full Flight Guided Writing CD

PDF CD versions of many titles also now available.

**See our full colour catalogue (available on request) or
visit our website for more information:** www.badger-publishing.co.uk

Contact us at:
Badger Publishing Limited
15 Wedgwood Gate, Pin Green Industrial Estate,
Stevenage, Hertfordshire SG1 4SU
Telephone: 01438 356907
Fax: 01438 747015
enquiries@badger-publishing.co.uk

Or visit our showroom and bookshop at the above address.